Contents

Harriet's Hare

Harriet's Hare by Dick King-Smith tells the story of a young girl, Harriet, who wakes one day to find a crop circle in her father's wheatfield. The alien that made the crop circle has taken on the form of a hare, and in this extract, Harriet meets the hare for the first time...

The farmhouse and its buildings were tucked into the side of a gentle hill, and in the little flat valley below were two large fields, the nearer one green, the further one gold.

In the first, her father's cows would normally have been waiting around
5 the gateway for him to come and fetch them in for morning milking. But now the whole herd was galloping and buck-jumping around the pasture as though something had scared the wits out of them.

The second field was of wheat, almost ready for harvesting, that looked from the house above like a square golden blanket, glowing in the morning
10 sunlight. But there seemed to be a hole in the blanket. In one corner of the wheatfield, Harriet could see, there was a perfect circle of flattened corn.

It took Harriet a quarter of an hour to dress and slip out of the house and run down the dewy hillside. By now the cows had quietened, and she ran through them to the wheatfield beyond, climbed over its gate and pushed
15 through the standing corn to step into that perfect circle.

What had made it? What had made the noise that had woken her and terrified the cows? Whatever had happened in the field called Ten Acre on Longhanger Farm at the start of this July day?

Harriet walked into the middle of the circle. It was big, perhaps twenty
20 metres across, and all the corn in it was squashed down to the ground, flat, as though an enormously heavy weight had rested there.

As she stood there now, in the stillness, with no sound but distant birdsong, a hare suddenly came out into the corn circle and stopped and sat up. It
25 turned its head a little sideways, the better to see her.

[...]

For a moment the hare stayed where it was, watching her. Then, to her great surprise, it lolloped right up to her.

Surprise is one thing, but total amazement is
30 quite another, and that was what Harriet next felt when all of a sudden the hare said, loudly and clearly, 'Good morning.'

An extract from *Harriet's Hare* by Dick King-Smith.

1 Why is one field described as green and the other as gold?

....

....

1 mark

2 What is unusual about the behaviour of the cows in the second paragraph?

....

....

2 marks

3 Why is the wheatfield described as a "square golden blanket" in line 9?
Why does the author say "there seemed to be a hole in the blanket" in line 10?

....

....

....

2 marks

4 Why does Harriet run out to the wheatfield?

....

1 mark

5 The hillside is described as "dewy" (line 13). What does this mean?
Use a dictionary to help you.

....

1 mark

6 Why do you think the author uses lots of questions in lines 16-18?

....

....

1 mark

7 Why does Harriet feel "great surprise" (line 27) and then "total amazement" (line 29)?

....

2 marks

....

Total
out of 10

....

Building Stonehenge

This extract is from a book about British history. Located in Wiltshire in the south of England, Stonehenge is one of the best-known prehistoric monuments in the world. It is an impressive structure and a popular tourist attraction, but how and why it was built remains a mystery...

The early Britons were so good at building structures from stone that some are still standing today. No one really knows what these strange structures were used for, but many archaeologists believe they were made to celebrate the changing seasons or to worship the sun.

5 Stonehenge is a prehistoric structure, found in Wiltshire, that is made up of a ring of vertical slabs of stone. Here is a brief history of the three main phases of its construction.

Stonehenge I

By around 3100 BC, people using deer antlers to break the earth dug a ditch about
10 2 metres deep and roughly 6 metres wide, forming a circle 98 metres across. Two tall stones marked the entrance on the northeast side of the circle. A wooden henge (which means a circular area) may also have been built at this time.

Stonehenge II

A bigger and better henge was built around 2300 BC. About 80 stones, each
15 weighing up to four tonnes, were placed upright in the centre of the site, forming another two circles. The stones were brought about 380 kilometres from a quarry in Wales — but no one really knows how. Many of the stones were carefully angled to line up with the position of the sun at different times of the year.

Stonehenge III

20 Around 2000 BC, more work was carried out and a new circle, with a horseshoe-shape of large stones, was created. A ring of 30 upright stones, weighing up to 50 tonnes each and standing up
25 to 9 metres tall, were added, and these were connected by a ring of stones that were laid on top.

An extract from *Off With Their Heads! All the Cool Bits in British History* by Martin Oliver.

1 What makes the author think that early Britons were good at building stone structures?

....

☐ 1 mark

2 Give two reasons why archaeologists believe the stone structures were built.

....

....

....

☐ 2 marks

3 Which of these statements are true about the stones used around 2300 BC? Circle two.

a. They weighed up to 4 tonnes.

b. They were brought from Scotland.

c. They were placed horizontally.

d. They formed another two circles.

☐ 2 marks

4 What connected the ring of thirty stones added around 2000 BC?

....

☐ 1 mark

5 How does this text's layout help to make it easier to read?

....

....

....

☐ 2 marks

6 Having read the text, would you like to visit Stonehenge? Explain your answer.

....

☐ 2 marks

....

Total
out of 10

☐

....

Nature Trail

Nature Trail was written by the poet, author and playwright Benjamin Zephaniah. Zephaniah enjoys being close to nature and animals, and in this poem, he describes all the wildlife that he sees in his garden. He encourages us to think about the importance of having a garden.

At the bottom of my garden
There's a hedgehog and a frog
And a lot of creepy-crawlies
Living underneath a log,
5 There's a baby daddy long legs
And an easy-going snail
And a family of woodlice,
All are on my nature trail.

There are caterpillars waiting
10 For their time to come to fly,
There are worms turning the earth over
As ladybirds fly by,
Birds will visit, cats will visit
But they always chose their time
15 And I've even seen a fox visit
This wild garden of mine.

Squirrels come to nick my nuts
And busy bees come buzzing
And when the night time comes
20 Sometimes some dragonflies come humming,
My garden mice are very shy
And I've seen bats that growl
And in my garden I have seen
A very wise old owl.

25 My garden is a lively place
There's always something happening,
There's this constant search for food
And then there's all that flowering,
When you have a garden
30 You will never be alone
And I believe we all deserve
A garden of our own.

Benjamin Zephaniah

1 Where do the creepy-crawlies live?

....

1 mark

2 Why do you think the poet describes the snail as "easy-going" (line 6)?

....

1 mark

3 Which two animals pick carefully when to visit the garden? Why do you think this is?

....

....

....

2 marks

4 Which animal does the author seem most surprised to have seen in his garden?

....

1 mark

5 Write down one word that has a similar meaning to "nick" (line 17).

....

1 mark

6 What two things does the poet say are always happening in his garden?

....

....

2 marks

7 Why do you think the poet believes "we all deserve a garden of our own" (lines 31-32)?

....

2 marks

....

Total
out of 10

....

Bill's New Frock

Bill's New Frock tells the story of Bill Simpson, a boy who wakes up one morning to find that he has become a girl. Bill is surprised to discover that boys and girls are treated very differently. In this extract, Bill realises that he has turned into a girl, but no one else seems to notice...

When Bill Simpson woke up on Monday morning, he found he was a girl.

He was still standing staring at himself in the mirror, quite baffled, when his mother swept in.

'Why don't you wear this pretty pink dress?' she said.

5   'I *never* wear dresses,' Bill burst out.

'I know,' his mother said. 'It's such a pity.'

And, to his astonishment, before he could even begin to argue, she had dropped the dress over his head and zipped up the back.

'I'll leave you to do up the shell buttons,' she said. 'They're a bit fiddly
10   and I'm late for work.'

And she swept out, leaving him staring in dismay at the mirror. In it, a girl with his curly red hair and wearing a pretty pink frock with fiddly shell buttons was staring back at him in equal dismay.

'This can't be true,' Bill Simpson said to himself. 'This cannot be true!'

15   He stepped out of his bedroom just as his father was rushing past. He, too, was late in getting off to work.

Mr Simpson leaned over and planted a kiss on Bill's cheek.

'Bye, Poppet,' he said, ruffling Bill's curls. 'You look very sweet today. It's not often we see you in a frock, is it?'

20   He ran down the stairs and out of the house so quickly he didn't see Bill's scowl, or hear what he muttered savagely under his breath.

Bella the cat didn't seem to notice any difference. She purred and rubbed her soft furry body around his ankles in exactly the same way as she always did.

And Bill found himself spooning up his cornflakes as usual. It was as if
25   he couldn't help it. He left the house at the usual time, too. He didn't seem to have any choice. Things, though odd, were just going on in their own way, as in a dream.

Or it could be a nightmare! For hanging about on the corner was the gang of boys from the other school. Bill recognised the one they called Mean
30   Malcolm in his purple studded jacket.

An extract from *Bill's New Frock* by Anne Fine.

1 What does the word "baffled" in line 2 mean? Use a dictionary to help you.

....

1 mark

2 What do Bill's mother's comments about wearing dresses tell us about her attitude towards girls?

....

....

1 mark

3 Why do you think Bill doesn't argue with his parents when they start treating him like a girl?

....

....

....

2 marks

4 How is Bella the cat's behaviour towards Bill different to his parents' behaviour?

....

....

2 marks

5 Explain why Bill says that what he's experiencing "could be a nightmare" (line 28).

....

....

....

2 marks

6 How might the children at Bill's school treat him differently now that he's a girl?

....

2 marks

....

Total
out of 10

....

Let's Get Growing!

This extract is from a gardening book for children by garden writer Lia Leendertz and children's television gardener Chris Collins, who has appeared on *Blue Peter*. In this extract, the authors write about how to get involved in gardening and the benefits that gardening can bring.

Let's get growing!

On a sunny spring morning, I cannot wait to get outside and check the seedlings that I planted a few days before. It's so exciting! Whether you plant one special sunflower or a whole plot of
5 **vegetables, seeing things grow is one of the real wonders of life.**

What if I haven't got a garden?

You don't need masses of space or even a garden to be a great gardener – a window-box can give you fresh herbs for pizzas, pasta, salads and sandwiches. Why not try growing a strawberry fountain or use a hanging basket to grow
10 tomatoes? They are great fun to grow and things you pick from your own plants are going to be fresher and far more tasty than anything you can buy in the shops. There is nothing like it. Remember though, give your plants a little bit of your time every day – don't forget to feed, water and give your plants lots of love.

Be a wildlife warrior

15 When you dig a piece of ground or turn over the soil to take out weeds and stones, it's great fun to watch how many birds you attract to your veg plot. Bees, butterflies, and other helpful insects can be encouraged to visit your garden by planting certain flowers. In turn, these insects will help your plants to grow by spreading pollen and seeds and eating pests. If you work with wildlife, they will
20 do a lot of the work for you.

So now you're a gardener

As you pick your first fruit and veg, you will see what fun it is to grow things. Everyone loves to be given great things to eat, but don't forget that you can give away some of your baby plants as well – in that way even more people can have
25 fun gardening. Being a gardener will keep you and your friends busy, happy and well fed and there's no better way to enjoy the great world outdoors.

An extract from *Grow Your Own for Kids* by Chris Collins and Lia Leendertz.

1 In what ways are the title and the first paragraph different from the rest of the text? Why do you think this is?

....

....

....

2 marks

2 Why do the authors recommend home-grown produce?

....

....

2 marks

3 What do you think the authors mean by "give your plants lots of love" in line 13?

....

....

1 mark

4 How do the authors feel about gardening? How can you tell?

....

....

....

2 marks

5 What do you think the purpose of this text is?

....

1 mark

6 Do you think being a gardener is important? Explain your answer.

....

2 marks

....

Total
out of 10

....

Daddy Fell into the Pond

Alfred Noyes was a poet who was born in 1880. *Daddy Fell into the Pond* was published in 1952. It is a comic poem which begins with a group of people having a dull day. However, everyone's mood is suddenly lifted when something unexpected happens...

Everyone grumbled. The sky was grey.

We had nothing to do and nothing to say.

We were nearing the end of a dismal day,

And there seemed to be nothing beyond,

5   THEN

        Daddy fell into the pond!

And everyone's face grew merry and bright,

And Timothy danced for sheer delight.

"Give me the camera, quick, oh quick!

10 He's crawling out of the duckweed."

          Click!

Then the gardener suddenly slapped his knee,

And doubled up, shaking silently,

And the ducks all quacked as if they were daft

15 And it sounded as if the old drake* laughed.

O, there wasn't a thing that didn't respond

         WHEN

        Daddy fell into the pond!

Alfred Noyes

Glossary

drake — male duck

1) Do you think the people are enjoying themselves in lines 1-4? Explain your answer.

....

....

2 marks

2) Why do you think the word "nothing" is repeated in line 2?

....

1 mark

3) Why do you think the poet put "THEN" in capitals and on a separate line in line 5?

....

....

1 mark

4) What does "Click!" in line 11 refer to?

....

1 mark

5) How do you think the gardener felt when "Daddy fell into the pond"? How can you tell?

....

....

....

2 marks

6) Which two words does the poet use to rhyme with "pond"?

....

1 mark

7) Describe how you think you would react if you saw someone fall into a pond.

....

2 marks

....

Total
out of 10

....

The Demon Headmaster

The Demon Headmaster is a novel by Gillian Cross. It tells the story of Dinah Glass and her foster brothers, Lloyd and Harvey. In this extract, Dinah attends her new school for the first time, but there's something strange about the way the other children are behaving...

It was a big playground, full of groups of strange children. No one so much as glanced at Dinah and she felt very awkward. But she was not a person who showed her feelings. Her pinched mouth did not relax for a moment. She looked round, wondering if there were any games she could join in. She thought there would be football, skipping,

5   and Tig*. And lots of people shouting and telling the latest crazy jokes from Friday night's Eddy Hair Show.

But it was not like that at all. All the children were standing in small neat circles in different parts of the playground, muttering. Carefully Dinah sidled up to* the first circle, trying to catch what the voices were saying. When she heard, she could hardly believe it.

10   'Nine twenty-ones are a hundred and eighty-nine,
Ten twenty-ones are two hundred and ten,
Eleven twenty-ones are two hundred and thirty-one...'

Extraordinary! She left them to it and moved across to another group, wondering if they were doing something more interesting. But they seemed to be reciting too. Only

15   what they were saying was different.

'William the First 1066 to 1087,
William the Second 1087 to 1100,
Henry the First 1100 to 1135...'

She stood beside them for some time, but they did not waver or look round at her.

20   They just went on chanting, their faces earnest. Behind her she could hear a third group. There, the children were muttering the names of the capitals of different countries.

'The capital of France is Paris,
The capital of Spain is Madrid,
The capital of the United States is—'

25   'New York,' said a little girl's voice.

'Lucy!' A bigger girl took her by the shoulder and shook her. 'You know that's not right. Come on, quickly. What is it?'

'I can't—I can't remember,' Lucy said in a scared voice. 'You know I've been away. Tell me. Please, Julie.'

Glossary	
Tig — a chasing game	sidled up to — went up to

An extract from
The Demon Headmaster by Gillian Cross.

1 Why do you think Dinah feels "very awkward" (line 2) when she arrives in the playground?

....
....

1 mark

2 How does Dinah expect children to behave in a playground?

....
....

2 marks

3 Why does Dinah find the children's behaviour surprising?

....
....
....

2 marks

4 What do you think the word "earnest" means in line 20? Circle one.

a. happy   b. calm   c. grumpy   d. serious

1 mark

5 How can you tell that the children in the second group are concentrating?

....
....
....

2 marks

6 How does Lucy feel when she can't remember the capital of the United States? Why do you think she feels this way?

....

2 marks

....

Total
out of 10

....

Robotic Baby Penguin

Scientists and engineers are designing robots that can be used in many different areas of life. This article is about a robot which looks like a penguin chick. Researchers designed this robot to help them get closer to emperor penguins and find out more about their behaviour.

Robotic baby penguin helps researchers get closer to shy adults

A tiny grey robotic penguin with four, thick, snow-ready black wheels is helping scientists to understand the species' behaviour.

5 As emperor penguins are notoriously* shy creatures, they retreat* when researchers approach them – causing their heart rates to rise and interfering with data on their health.

10 To tackle this problem, a team of scientists and film-makers led by Yvon Le Maho of the University of Strasbourg in France created a remote control rover* disguised as a chick. The cunningly designed robot
15 can easily sidle up to* penguins without scaring them away.

The robot has been deployed* in Adelie Land, Antarctica, where the 2005 documentary *March of the Penguins*
20 was filmed, and allowed researchers to study the animals from over 650 feet (200 meters) away.

But to create the successful bot, scientists endured a process of trial and error, with
25 the first disguised version of the rover,

made of fibreglass scaring the real birds, Le Maho said.

Researchers tried about five versions before they found their final design which
30 is covered in grey fur, sports black arms, and has a black-and-white painted face and black beak.

"The penguins did not scamper away and even sang to it with "a very special song
35 like a trumpet," Le Maho said.

Le Maho suggested that the adult penguins were trying to find a mate for their chicks and they were listening for a response, but researchers didn't program the rover to
40 make a sound.

"They were very disappointed when there was no answer," Le Maho said. "Next time we will have a rover playing songs."

Abridged article from
www.independent.co.uk

Glossary		
notoriously — famously	rover — vehicle	deployed — used
retreat — run away	sidle up to — go up to	

1 Why do the researchers need to use a robot when they study the penguins?

....

....

....

2 marks

2 The word "cunningly" on line 14 is (circle one):

a. a noun   b. a preposition   c. a verb   d. an adverb

1 mark

3 Where has the robotic penguin been used, according to the text?

....

1 mark

4 What shortened form of the word 'robot' is used in the text?

....

1 mark

5 Do you think it is easy or difficult to design a robot that can be used to help researchers study penguins? Explain your answer.

....

....

....

2 marks

6 Why did the penguins find the robot disappointing?

....

....

1 mark

7 How do you think Yvon Le Maho felt when he saw the robotic penguin go up to the real penguins without scaring them? Explain your answer.

....

2 marks

....

Total
out of 10

....

High Adventure

Mount Everest is the highest mountain in the world. In 1953, Edmund Hillary and Tenzing Norgay were the first people to climb to the top of Mount Everest. This is an extract from Edmund Hillary's book about this adventure. It describes the first time Hillary saw a mountain.

I was sixteen before I ever saw a mountain. My father's rapidly expanding bee business had occupied all my holidays, and I'd learned to do a full-size job before I entered my teens. But in the winter of 1935 I'd saved a little money and I was allowed to join a School Ski-ing Party
5   to Ruapehu – one of our large New Zealand volcanoes. I was in the Lower Sixth Form at the time – a tall, bony, clumsy-looking youth, far from being the brightest lad in the class; and I don't think I'd been more than fifty miles outside of Auckland. I'd heard glowing tales from the other boys about ski-ing holidays, but it didn't mean a great deal to me
10   – all I wanted was a chance to see the world.

I saw my first snow at midnight when we stepped off our train at the National Park station. There wasn't much of it but it was a tremendous thrill, and before long snowballs, as hard as iron, were flying through the air. And as our bus carried us steadily up towards the Château*,
15   perched high on the mountain-side, its powerful lights sparked into life a fairy-land of glistening snow and stunted pines and frozen streams. When I crawled into my bunk at two in the morning, I felt I was in a strange and exciting new world.

For ten glorious days we skied and played on the lower slopes of the
20   mountain, and I don't think I ever looked towards the summit*. We had been told the upper parts of the mountain were dangerous, and I viewed them with respect and fear. I never dared to venture* on them. I returned home in a glow of fiery enthusiasm for the sun and the cold and the snow – especially the snow!

An extract from *High Adventure* by Sir Edmund Hillary (2003): pp.1-2 Oxford University Press

<u>Glossary</u>		
Château — castle	summit — the top of a mountain	to venture — to risk going

1 Why did Edmund want to go on the ski trip?

....

....

2 marks

2 How do you think Edmund felt when he reached the National Park station? Explain your answer.

....

....

....

2 marks

3 What phrase does Edmund use to describe the snowballs?

....

1 mark

4 Why do you think Edmund describes the mountain as "a fairy-land" (line 16)?

....

....

....

2 marks

5 Give one reason why Edmund didn't go onto the upper parts of the mountain during the trip.

....

1 mark

6 As an adult, Edmund Hillary became a mountaineer and explorer.
Do you think this ski trip influenced his choice of career? Explain your answer.

....

2 marks

....

....

Total
out of 10

An Interview with Rebecca Adlington

Rebecca Adlington had a very successful career as a competitive swimmer. She won two gold medals at the 2008 Olympics in Beijing, and two bronze medals at the 2012 Olympics in London. In this interview, she talks about how she got into swimming and why she loves it.

When did you get into swimming?

When I was younger, my parents took me and my older sisters to swimming lessons so that when we went on holiday, they could leave us in the pool without being scared. Swimming with my older sisters gave me extra motivation as I always wanted to keep up
5 with them.

When did you decide you wanted to compete?

I joined a club when I was eight or nine, but I didn't start racing until I was 10 or 11. My first big competition was the European Youth Olympic Festival in 2003, when I was 14. After that, I thought I can really do this. After my GCSEs, I took a year off to focus on
10 competitive swimming and I haven't looked back.

What do you love about swimming?

There's something uniquely fun about being in the water. There's nothing like it. Everyone should experience it. I love being in the water, whether
15 I'm competing or not.

How does swimming keep you healthy?

Swimming works every muscle group in your body, but it's kind to your joints. The risk of injury is very low compared to other sports. So it's healthy and safe. There's no upper age limit for a swimmer. At my local pool at 7am, you'll see the older guys swimming next
20 to schoolchildren. It's a wonderful contrast and shows that swimming is for everyone.

What's your training routine?

I do about 10 sessions a week, at two-and-a-half hours each. All I do is sleep, train, drive and occasionally find time to eat.

What's your advice on staying motivated?

25 I train with a squad of 20 people and that really helps. We're all friends and we push each other. My advice is to go swimming with a friend regularly. Having someone to swim with will encourage you to swim on days when you're lacking motivation. It's also good to mix things up. Practise different strokes, use kickboards to work your legs, set yourself little targets such as increasing the number of lengths you can do or improving certain areas of
30 your technique.

From *http://www.nhs.uk/Livewell/fitness/Pages/rebecca-adlington.aspx*

1 In your own words, explain why Rebecca's parents wanted her to learn to swim.

....

....

1 mark

2 Why does Rebecca think that swimming is a sport that anyone can enjoy?

....

1 mark

3 How much time does Rebecca usually spend training each week?

....

1 mark

4 Write down two things that you think motivate Rebecca to spend so much time training.

....

....

2 marks

5 Which of the following pieces of advice was not suggested by Rebecca as a way to help people stay motivated? Circle one.

a. set targets

b. go swimming regularly

c. swim with people of different ages

d. vary your training

1 mark

6 Do you think Rebecca has a competitive personality? Explain your answer.

....

....

2 marks

7 Do you think this interview would persuade people to do more swimming? Explain your answer.

....

....

2 marks

Total
out of 10

My Name is Mina

My Name is Mina is a novel by British author David Almond. The main character is a nine-year-old girl called Mina. The book is written in the form of Mina's diary. In this extract, Mina starts keeping a diary for the first time, and thinks about what she wants to write in it.

There's an empty notebook lying on the table in the moonlight. It's been there for an age. I keep on saying that I'll write a journal. So I'll start right here, right now. I open the book and write the very first words:

MY NAME IS MINA AND I LOVE THE NIGHT.

5   Then what shall I write? I can't just write that this happened then this happened then this happened to boring infinitum*. I'll let my journal grow just like the mind does, just like a tree or a beast does, just like life does. Why should a book tell a tale in a dull straight line?

Words should wander and meander*. They should fly like owls and
10   flicker like bats and slip like cats. They should murmur and scream and dance and sing.

Sometimes there should be no words at all.

Just silence.

Just clean white space.

15   Some pages will be like a sky with a single bird in it. Some will be like a sky with a swirling swarm of starlings in it. My sentences will be a clutch*, a collection, a pattern, a swarm, a shoal, a mosaic. They will be a circus, a menagerie*, a tree, a nest. Because my mind is not in order. My mind is not straight lines. My mind is a clutter and a mess. It is my mind, but it is also
20   very like other minds. And like all minds, like every mind that there has ever been and every mind that there will ever be, it is a place of wonder.

An extract from *My Name is Mina* by David Almond.

Glossary	
infinitum — forever	a clutch — a group
meander — follow a winding path	a menagerie — a collection of unusual animals

1 Is it daytime or night-time in this extract? How can you tell?

....

....

2 marks

2 Why do you think line 4 is written differently to the rest of the text?

....

1 mark

3 What does Mina mean by "clean white space" (line 14)?

....

....

1 mark

4 What do you think a page "like a sky with a single bird in it" (line 15) would look like?

....

....

1 mark

5 The word "swarm" on line 17 is (circle one):

a. a verb   b. a proper noun   c. a collective noun   d. an adverb

1 mark

6 Why does Mina say "My mind is not straight lines" (lines 18-19)?

....

....

2 marks

7 Write down one adjective to describe Mina's personality. Explain your choice.

....

2 marks

....

Total
out of 10

....

Poems about Crocodiles

Crocodiles live in tropical parts of Africa, Asia, Australia and the Americas, but there aren't any wild crocodiles in Britain. Many people are frightened of crocodiles because they can grow to be extremely large. They also have very powerful jaws and lots of sharp teeth.

How Doth the Little Crocodile

How doth the little crocodile

Improve his shining tail,

And pour the waters of the Nile

On every golden scale!

5   How cheerfully he seems to grin,

How neatly spreads his claws,

And welcomes little fishes in,

With gently smiling jaws!

Lewis Carroll

If You Should Meet a Crocodile

If you should meet a crocodile

Don't take a stick and poke him;

Ignore the welcome in his smile,

Be careful not to stroke him.

5   For as he sleeps upon the Nile,

He thinner gets and thinner;

And whene'er you meet a crocodile

He's ready for his dinner.

Christine F. Fletcher

1 Is Carroll's poem written in the first person or the third person?

....

1 mark

2 Which word do both poets use to rhyme with "crocodile"?

....

1 mark

3 a. Which verb in line 5 of Carroll's poem describes
the expression on the crocodile's face?

....

1 mark

b. Which noun in line 3 of Fletcher's poem describes a similar expression?

....

1 mark

4 Which adjective is used more than once in Fletcher's poem?

....

1 mark

5 What is the crocodile in Carroll's poem actually doing when he "welcomes little fishes in"?

....

1 mark

6 Why shouldn't you stroke a crocodile, according to Fletcher's poem?

....

....

2 marks

7 Many people are frightened of crocodiles. Do you think the crocodile
in Carroll's poem sounds frightening? Explain your answer.

....

2 marks

....

....

Total
out of 10

The Secret History of Tom Trueheart

The Secret History of Tom Trueheart is a novel by Ian Beck. It is set in the *Land of Stories*. The main character, Tom Trueheart, has six brothers who are all brave adventurers. In this extract, the reader meets Tom for the first time, and finds out about his worrying secret...

Once upon a time, long ago, near the Land of Stories, lived young Tom Trueheart. He was the youngest of the famous Trueheart family of adventurers. He lived far away from here, and even further from now, in a carved and painted wooden house near a busy crossroads, on the edge of a deep dark forest, in the

5   time of fables. He lived with his kindly mother, and with his six older brothers.

Tom's six older brothers were all named Jack.

It was these brave brothers, these same six, fabled, heroic Jacks who had carried out all of the toughest, scariest, and most romantic and exciting adventures so far to have happened in the Land of Stories.

10   All of the great stories had happened to a Jack.

Over the years, the youngest son Tom Trueheart had grown into an imaginative, kind, and helpful boy. He was not tall or broad for his age, as all his brothers had been, he was slight and wiry. His hair was dark and curled naturally, while all his brothers had hair which was straight and worn long like

15   a Viking warrior.

From the earliest age he had suffered from bad dreams after listening to all the scary adventure stories of his older brothers. Dreams of wolves waiting in the darkest parts of the forest with big teeth and dripping jaws. Dreams of Ogres and Giants and dark dungeons and black-cloaked, smiling villains. Even

20   when there was just Tom and his mother, and they had a rare quiet evening on their own together, she would insist that they huddled cosily side by side in the inglenook fireplace (the kind you can actually sit inside) and she couldn't resist telling him one or two of the old and really scary stories. Stories, after all, were the family trade...

25   There was just one thing: Tom carried in his heart a worrying secret. A secret he kept locked up very tight inside. He was not like his bigger brothers in one other very important way. *He was not at all brave.*

An abridged extract from *The Secret History of Tom Trueheart, Boy Adventurer* by Ian Beck.

1 Which noun in lines 2-5 means 'stories'?

....

1 mark

2 What does the phrase "even further from now" (line 3)
tell you about when this story is set?

....

....

1 mark

3 How many people live in the Truehearts' house?

....

1 mark

4 Tom's brothers are famous in the *Land of Stories*. Why do you think this is?

....

....

1 mark

5 Give two differences between the way Tom looks and the way his brothers look.

....

....

....

2 marks

6 Do you think Tom enjoys listening to adventure stories? Explain your answer.

....

....

2 marks

7 Why do you think Tom keeps it a secret that he is not brave?

....

2 marks

....

Total
out of 10

....

Jellyfish in the UK

Jellyfish have bell-shaped bodies and long tentacles or arms. Many jellyfish are harmless to humans, but some can sting. Jellyfish stings can cause serious pain and illness. This article is about the barrel jellyfish, a harmless jellyfish which is found in the seas around Britain.

Jellyfish in the UK: Huge blooms of barrel species found on coast after mini-heatwave

Scores of large jellyfish have been discovered on Britain's coastline after they have been attracted to warmer conditions brought on by a recent
5 mini-heatwave.

Blooms of barrel jellyfish – that can grow up to the size of a dustbin lid – have been spotted on the south coast after a summer-like climate made a brief
10 appearance.

The species can weigh up to 55lbs (24kgs) and have eight thick "arms", rather than tentacles, made from frilly-like tissue.

15 Although the jellyfish, which have no brain or bones, may appear frightening to some, they're actually harmless to humans as their stings are not strong enough to wound, however it is advised
20 to not touch them.

They live exclusively off plankton* that thrive in warm weather.

A video filmed from a fishing boat shows the blooms of jellyfish floating about not
25 far from Falmouth Bay in Cornwall.

The two heatwave days – which saw temperatures reach 25C and were hotter than some parts of the Mediterranean – are likely to have encouraged the rapid
30 growth of plankton in our waters.

A diver faced one of the tentacled creatures during an exploration in Plymouth Sound on Friday evening.

Todd Palmer told the *Plymouth Herald*:
35 "It's the biggest one I've seen. I was looking for nudibranchs* and just happened to look up and see it.

"I've seen three recently. They're not too rare but usually it's a sign of a good
40 summer."

Last year saw the most barrel jellyfish on the UK coast since 2002, according to nature website Bug Life.

One weighed just over 44lbs (20kgs),
45 which is impressive considering jellyfish consist of more than 90 per cent water.

If this summer is as warm as the last then the number of them could be even higher. In winter, the jellyfish usually
50 swim deeper and further away from the UK.

From *www.independent.co.uk*

Glossary

plankton — tiny creatures floating in the sea

nudibranch — a kind of sea slug

1 Write down a word that the author could have used instead of "scores" in line 1.

....

1 mark

2 Why do barrel jellyfish have more to eat when the weather is warm?

....

....

1 mark

3 According to the article, which two body parts do humans have that jellyfish don't?

....

2 marks

4 Why are fewer jellyfish found in British waters in the winter?

....

....

1 mark

5 Which adjective best describes this text? Circle one.

a. factual   b. persuasive   c. fictional   d. exciting

1 mark

6 Which two presentational features show that this text is a newspaper article?

....

....

2 marks

7 How do you think Todd might have felt when he looked up and saw a barrel jellyfish? Explain your answer.

....

2 marks

....

Total
out of 10

....

Carrie's War

Carrie's War by Nina Bawden is a novel set during World War Two. During the war, children living in English cities were sent to the countryside because cities were at risk of being bombed. In this extract, Carrie and her brother Nick are moving to Wales from their home in London.

He threw up all over Miss Fazackerly's skirt. He had been feeling sick ever since they left the main junction and climbed into the joggling, jolting little train for the last lap

5 of their journey, but the sudden whistle had finished him.

Such a noise — it seemed to split the sky open. 'Enough to frighten the dead,' Miss Fazackerly said, mopping her skirt and Nick's

10 face with her handkerchief. He lay back limp as a rag and let her do it, the way he always let people do things for him, not lifting a finger. 'Poor lamb', Miss Fazackerly said, but Carrie looked stern.

'It's all his own fault. He's been stuffing his face ever since we left London. Greedy pig. *Dustbin.*'

15 He had not only eaten his own packed lunch — sandwiches and cold sausages and bananas — but most of Carrie's as well. She had let him have it to comfort him because he minded leaving home and their mother more than she did. Or had looked as if he minded more. She thought now that it was just one of his acts, put on to get sympathy. Sympathy and chocolate! He had had all her

20 chocolate, too! 'I knew he'd be sick,' she said smugly.

'Might have warned me then, mightn't you?' Miss Fazackerly said. Not unkindly, she was one of the kindest teachers in the school, but Carrie wanted to cry suddenly. If she had been Nick she would have cried, or at least put on a hurt face. Being Carrie she stared crossly out of the carriage window at the big

25 mountain on the far side of the valley. It was brown and purple on the top and green lower down; streaked with silver trickles of water and dotted with sheep.

Sheep and mountains. 'Oh, it'll be such fun,' their mother had said when she kissed them good-bye at the station. 'Living in the country instead of the stuffy old city. You'll love it, you see if you don't!'

An extract from *Carrie's War* by Nina Bawden.

1 Find and copy a phrase from lines 7-12 which shows that the whistle was very loud.

....
1 mark

2 Was Miss Fazackerly angry with Nick for being sick on her skirt? How can you tell?

....

....
1 mark

3 Why did Carrie give her lunch to Nick?

....
1 mark

4 a. Carrie says "smugly" in line 20 that she knew Nick would be sick. What does 'smug' mean? Use a dictionary to help you.

....
1 mark

b. Why do you think Carrie was feeling smug?

....
1 mark

5 How does Carrie know Miss Fazackerly?

....
1 mark

6 Why do you think Nick and Carrie's mother told them that living in the country would be "such fun" (line 27)?

....

....
2 marks

7 How do you think Carrie and Nick would have felt being evacuated from home?

....
2 marks

....

....

Total
out of 10

The Lonely Dragon

By now, you've had plenty of practice at reading texts and answering questions. Now it's time to write your own text, think of some questions, and then swap with a friend.

Write a story about a lonely dragon. Think about how it feels to be lonely, and how the dragon might find some friends. We've made a start on the story, but what happens next is up to you!

Joel was walking home from school one day when he heard a strange snuffling sound coming from behind some trees. He went to investigate, and was astonished to find a small, orange dragon with tears streaming down its face.

"Why are you crying?" asked Joel.

E3CW21